Amazon
River Rescue

Adventures of Riley

Amazon River Rescue

Riley,

Greetings from the Amazon! I am on assignment to study the role that kapok trees play in supporting life in the rain forest. Your Aunt Martha and Cousin Alice are here with me collecting important bark and leaf samples.

We need you to come help us, since your endless curiosity always turns up something interesting! We all look forward to your arrival, especially Alice. She is lost without you!

Don't leave me hanging,

Uncle Max

BY
Amanda Lumry
AND **Laura Hurwitz**
ILLUSTRATED BY **Sarah McIntyre**

SCHOLASTIC INC.
New York • Toronto • London • Auckland • Sydney
Mexico City • New Delhi • Hong Kong • Buenos Aires

A special thank-you to all the scientists who collaborated on this project. Your time and assistance are very much appreciated.

First published in China in 2004 by Eaglemont Press.
www.eaglemont.com

All photographs by Amanda Lumry except:
Cover background © Will & Deni McIntyre/Getty Images
Page 4 scarlet macaw © Roy Toft/Getty Images
Page 4 toucan © Natphotos/Getty Images
Page 4 boa and page 14 sloth © Tom Brakefield/Getty Images
Page 4 coati © Art Wolfe/Getty Images
Page 5 anteater © Anup Shah/Getty Images
Page 9 capybaras © Nicole Duplaix/Getty Images
Pages 20–21 Amazon fire © Digital Vision/Getty Images
Page 23 jaguar © Jeff Foott/Getty Images

Illustrations © 2004 by Sarah McIntyre
Additional Illustrations and Layouts by Ulkutay & Ulkutay, London WC2E 9RZ
Editing and Digital Compositing by Michael E. Penman
Digital Imaging by Phoenix Color

Library of Congress Control Number: 2004005145

ISBN-13: 978-0-545-06855-0
ISBN-10: 0-545-06855-x

10 9 8 7 6 5 4 3 2 1   09 10 11 12 13

Printed in the U.S.A.   08
First Scholastic paperback printing, March 2009

FSC
Mixed Sources
Product group from well-managed forests, controlled sources and recycled wood or fiber
Cert no. SGS-COC-003338
www.fsc.org
© 1996 Forest Stewardship Council

A portion of the proceeds from your purchase of this licensed product supports the stated educational mission of the Smithsonian Institution— "the increase and diffusion of knowledge." The name of the Smithsonian Institution and the sunburst logo are registered trademarks of the Smithsonian Institution and are registered in the U.S. Patent and Trademark Office. www.si.edu

2% of the proceeds from this book will be donated to the Wildlife Conservation Society. http://wcs.org

A portion of the proceeds from your purchase of this product supports The Wyland Foundation, a 501(c)(3) nonprofit organization founded in 1993 by environmental marine life artist Wyland. By bridging the worlds of art and science, the Wyland Foundation strives to inspire people of all ages to become better stewards of our oceans and global water resources.
http://wylandfoundation.org
www.wyland.com

We try to produce the most beautiful books possible and we are extremely concerned about the impact of our manufacturing process on the forests of the world and the environment as a whole. Accordingly, we made sure that the paper used in this book has been certified as coming from forests that are managed to ensure the protection of the people and wildlife dependent upon them.

"I'm going to the Amazon rain forest tomorrow," Riley said to his friends. "I've heard it's full of man-eating piranhas, poisonous snakes, and who knows what else!"

"Have fun," said Mike. "But be careful!"

"I will," said Riley. He couldn't wait to go, but still he wondered, *If the Amazon is so full of amazing animals, why is Uncle Max studying trees?*

I

Amazon Rain Forest

➤ The Amazon rain forest is almost as big as the continental United States.

➤ If the Amazon Basin were a country, it would be the ninth largest in the world.

➤ Over 3,000 fish species are found in the Amazon River. Most of them do not exist anywhere else.

—Dr. William Laurance,
Staff Research Scientist,
Smithsonian Tropical
Research Institute

After traveling for hours on a plane and then a ferryboat, Riley arrived in the Amazon.

"Welcome to Brazil!" called Uncle Max. "I've just discovered a new fungus. I'm going to call it the Maximus Fungus."

MANAUS

"Wow!" said Riley.

"I'd rather have a nice animal or flower named after me," added Alice.

"With so many undiscovered species in the Amazon, you never know what you might find," said Aunt Martha. "Or what might find you!"

Toco Toucan

➤ Its huge beak is very light because it is filled with air.

➤ It can swallow fruit the size of a walnut.

—Dr. Gary R. Graves,
Research Zoologist & Curator of Birds,
National Museum of Natural History,
Smithsonian Institution

Tobaccomama Frog

➤ Its nest is a white ball of foam that floats on the water.

➤ People say it tastes like tobacco unless it is boiled first!

—A. Stanley Rand,
Senior Scientist Emeritus,
Smithsonian Tropical Research Institute

CANOPY

UNDERSTORY

4

Tamandua Anteater

➤ It does not have any teeth!

➤ Its sticky tongue helps it capture ants and termites.

—Dr. Kent Redford,
Vice President, Conservation Strategy,
Wildlife Conservation Society

Leaf-Cutter Ant

➤ Large soldier ants protect the queen.

➤ It chews leaves into pulp to fertilize **fungus** beds—its only source of food.

—Dr. Dan Wharton, Director,
Central Park Zoo,
Wildlife Conservation Society

"Why do you study trees?" asked Riley. "Wouldn't **prowling** jaguars, giant alligators, or even man-eating piranhas be more exciting?"

"Join me in the boat and I'll show you!" said Uncle Max. "Trees provide homes and food for animals and birds. Plus, we all breathe the oxygen that trees produce. Without trees, animals and humans couldn't **survive**."

Piranha

➤ It eats more than just meat—almost half of its diet is fruits and nuts.

➤ Many more humans have eaten piranha than the other way around.

—Dr. Paul Loiselle, Associate Curator,
Freshwater Fish, New York Aquarium,
Wildlife Conservation Society

FOREST
FLOOR

"Speaking of alligators, why don't we visit the caiman?" suggested Uncle Max, as the sun began to set. Several sets of glowing eyes watched them closely.

This is so spooky, thought Riley.

"BOO!" yelled Alice.

"Ahhh!" Riley jumped.

Caiman

➤ The sex of the young is determined by the temperature of the nest before the eggs hatch.

➤ It can grow to be 10 ft. (3 m) long!

➤ There are 23 different types of crocodile, alligator, and caiman in the world.

—Dr. Rosa Lemos de Sá, Conservation Director, World Wildlife Fund, Brazil

Riley's first night in the Amazon was a real eye-opening experience.

Riley and Alice got up early to play soccer.
After the game, they decided to go exploring.

They stopped at the edge of camp. Something was moving in the distance.

"What are those?" asked Riley.

"Let's climb down and see!" said Alice.

"What about the sign?" Riley asked, trying to be careful.

"Maybe they're undiscovered animals!" said Alice.

KEEP OUT

"They look like little bears!" said Alice. "I'm going to call them Alice Bears!"

"I think we should call them Rilesters," said Riley.

The mysterious animals jumped into the river and
began swimming away.

"We need a boat," said Riley.

"I know there's one back at camp," said Alice. "Follow
me."

"Are you sure this is the right way?" asked Riley.

"Of course it is," said Alice. But, of course, it wasn't.

After walking in circles, they spied a red rope tied to a funny-looking tree. At the end of the rope was a boat!

"Wait, don't move!" warned Riley.

Alice froze at the sight of a large, hairy tarantula. Riley scooped it up and set it on a tree branch far away.

Tarantula

➤ The largest tarantula is the size of a dinner plate and the smallest is tinier than a grain of rice.

➤ Even though it has eight eyes, it has bad eyesight.

➤ It can live as long as 30 years!

—Jonathan Coddington, Research Scientist, National Museum of Natural History, Smithsonian Institution

"There they are!" said Alice.

They paddled as fast as they could, but they couldn't keep up with the strange animals.

"Hey, there's a sloth," Riley said. "I think I'll call it an Alice Sloth."

"Very funny, Riley," Alice sighed. "Hey, look!"

Sloth

➤ Yes, it is slow, but it moves five times faster than a snail!

➤ It does everything (eating, sleeping, giving birth) hanging upside down . . . except for pooping!

➤ It is the only greenish-colored **mammal**. The color comes from the algae in its fur.

—Dr. Michael Valqui,
Mammalogist,
World Wildlife Fund, Peru

In front of them was a tower of smoke.

"That's way too much smoke for a campfire," said
Riley. "It looks more like . . ."

Riley's heart was pounding. They pulled the boat out of the water and scrambled up a tree to get a better view.

Amazon Rain Forest

➤ A rain forest is a large, thick forest full of many kinds of life and is found in tropical areas where it rains a lot.

➤ The Amazon rain forest provides 20% of the world's oxygen.

➤ The greatest threat to the Amazon rain forest is **deforestation**.

—Dr. John Robinson,
Senior Vice President and Director
for International Conservation,
Wildlife Conservation Society

"This isn't camp," said Alice.

"It's so quiet. The smoke and fire must have forced all the animals and birds away," said Riley. The wind changed, blowing a cloud of smoke in their direction.

"Quick, let's get back to the boat!" Alice coughed.

19

"Alice, I hear a helicopter!" said Riley.

"Do you think that's my parents?" asked Alice. "I bet they were worried when we didn't show up for lunch."

"Oh no! I don't think they can see us through the smoke!" said Riley. *So much for being careful*, he thought.

Jaguar

➤ Yes, it can swim!

➤ It is the largest cat in North and South America.

➤ Early South American cultures worshipped it as a god.

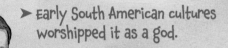

—Dr. Alan Rabinowitz, Director, Science and Exploration, Wildlife Conservation Society

"This can't get any worse," groaned Alice.

"Yes, it can," breathed Riley. "Look!"

"A JAGUAR! And jaguars can swim!" said Alice.

They both sat very still and watched the big cat. It paced back and forth, sniffing the smoky air before slipping into the bush.

"Whew! We were seconds away from becoming jaguar jerky!" said Alice.

"If we're going to get home before dark, we have to come up with a plan. Look for anything **familiar**," Riley said.

Nothing looked **familiar** to Alice at all. NOTHING. They paddled and paddled around curve after curve and by tree after tree. Then she saw it!

"Hooray!" Alice yelled. "There's the red rope tied to that funny-looking tree!"

"Great spotting!" said Riley. "It's getting dark. We'll have to camp here for the night."

"Terrific. Just what I wanted to do, sleep under a giant kapok tree," said Alice.

"Did you say KAPOK?" Riley asked. "I have an idea. Grab your paddle!"

26

Kapok Tree

➤ It can grow 10 ft. (3 m) in height in one year.

➤ It is the tallest tree in the Amazon rain forest.

➤ Its wood is used to make furniture.

➤ It is home to many animals.

➤ Its flowers are **pollinated** by bats.

—Maxwell Plimpton,
Professor,
Senior Field Biologist

"I've read about chimpanzees doing this in Africa," Riley said.

"Doing what?" Alice asked. Riley started banging on the roots of the tree, and a loud, booming sound echoed throughout the river basin.

"Doing this!" He grinned.

27

After several minutes of *knock-knock-knocking*, the kapok lit up like a Christmas tree.

"Who's there?" asked the tree.

That voice . . . could it be? It was! Standing on a walkway high above them was Uncle Max, spotlight in hand, with a smile as wide as the Amazon River.

"Looks like Aunt Martha was right. You never know what you'll find in the Amazon!" he said.

"We were worried sick about you!" cried Aunt Martha.

"Trees are saving our lives all the time," remarked
Uncle Max, "but tonight this tree played a starring role."

"We were trying to follow a furry new animal called the Alice Bear," said Alice.

"I think you mean the *Rilester*," said Riley.

"Actually, it was a capybara," said Uncle Max. "That **rodent** is quite common around here and was discovered, and named, a long time ago."

"Oh," the children said sadly.

Capybara

➤ Its nostrils are high on its head so it can hide underwater and still breathe.

➤ It is the world's largest **rodent** and can weigh up to 140 lb. (65 kg).

➤ Its feet are partially webbed.

—Meg Symington, Director, Forests and Freshwater, World Wildlife Fund, Latin America

As they walked inside, a small bug landed on Riley's shirt.

"Incredible!" cried Uncle Max. "I've never seen an insect like this before."

"I bet it's an undiscovered bug!" Riley said. They studied it closely for several minutes, then it flew off into the night.

"There goes the Alice Beetle!" gasped Alice.

"Don't you mean the Riley Roach?" Riley grinned. That night they all dreamed of making new discoveries of their own.

INSECTS
An Amazon
Field Guide

31

Back home at soccer practice, Riley thrilled everyone with stories of the "Riley Roach" and being lost in the Amazon. He returned to living the life of a nine-year-old . . . until he got another letter from his Uncle Max.

Where will Riley go next?

FURTHER INFORMATION

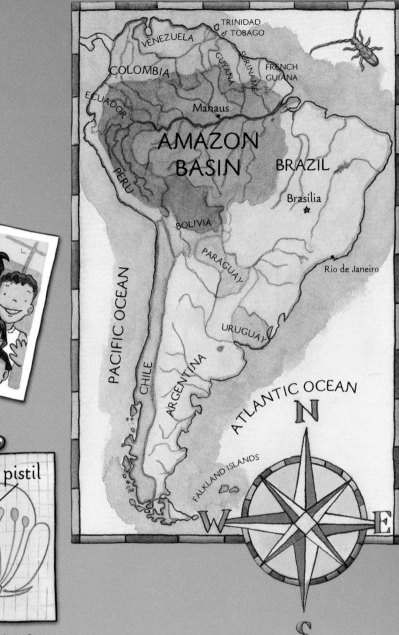

Glossary

deforestation: the process of destroying trees by burning or cutting them down

familiar: well-known, often seen, common

fungus: molds, mildews, and mushrooms that grow without the help of the sun or true root systems

mammal: a warm-blooded creature with a spine, fed by milk from its mother

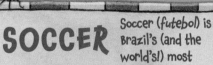

stamen   pistil

pollinated: moved the fine dust produced in seed plants from the stamen to the pistil of the flower so that it can bloom

prowling: roaming around, often in search of prey

rodent: a small mammal, such as a mouse, rat, or squirrel, known for using its sharp teeth to chew

survive: to continue to live or exist

SOCCER

Soccer (*futebol*) is Brazil's (and the world's!) most popular sport. The Brazilian National Team has won many World Cup titles.

Pelé, the most famous soccer player of all time, is from Brazil. Pelé first played soccer in neighborhood games called *peladas*, using rolled-up rags instead of balls.

Soccer is everywhere in Brazil! You will even find people playing soccer in clearings in the heart of the Amazon rain forest.

Illustration: Pelé and Ronaldo, popular Brazilian soccer stars.

JOIN US FOR MORE GREAT ADVENTURES!

Visit our Web site at
www.adventuresofriley.com
to find out how
you can join Riley's
super kids' club!

Look for these other great Riley books:

➤ Outback Odyssey
➤ Riddle of the Reef
➤ Operation Orangutan
➤ Survival of the Salmon